The lost truck

Story written by Karra McFarlane

Illustrated by Brian Fitzgerald

Sam has lost his truck.

"Is it black?" said Pip.

"No, it's red," said Sam.

"Is it next to the hut?"
said Pip.

"No, that's not it."

"What is in it?" said Kat.

"It's full of mud."

"Is it next to the mud pit?" said Kat.

"No, that's not it."

"Is it a big truck?" said Jim.

"Yes, it's a tip-up truck."

"Is it in the pond?" said Jim.

"Yes, that's it!"

Retell the story

Take turns retelling the story with your child.